MAD®
BOOK OF ALMOST SUPERHEROES

Written and Illustrated by
DON EDWING

Edited by
Nick Meglin

WARNER BOOKS

A Warner Communications Company

Dedicated to **Claire Kathleen Harrigan**
who is an ALMOST SUPERHERO herself!

WARNER BOOKS EDITION

Copyright © 1982 by Don Edwing
and E.C. Publications, Inc.

All rights reserved.
No part of this book may be reproduced without permission.
For information address E.C. Publications, Inc.,
485 Madison Avenue, New York, N.Y. 10022

Title ''MAD'' used with permission of its owner.
E.C. Publications, Inc.

This Warner Books Edition is published by
arrangement with E.C. Publications, Inc.

Warner Books, Inc.,
75 Rockefeller Plaza,
New York, N.Y. 10019

A Warner Communications Company

Printed in the United States of America

First Printing: April, 1982

10 9 8 7 6 5 4 3 2 1

Table of Characters

Ms. *Wonder Blunder*

THE DOLTING,
DARING, DARLING,
SUPER HEROINE
DEDICATED TO
FIGHT CRIME,
GET A HUSBAND,
AND LOSE WEIGHT!

The *PINK FRUITFLY*

THE DOLTING,
DARING, DARLING,
SUPERHERO
DEDICATED
TO ALL OF THE
ABOVE!

RAGOO of the JUNGLE

THE GOURMET
OF ALL COMICDOM!
RENOWN FOR HIS—
WHAT ELSE—
RAGOO SAUCE!

THE *SCARLET PIMPLE*

HE'S HERE!
HE'S THERE!
HE'S EVERYWHERE!
EXCEPT WHERE
HE'S NEEDED!

CAPTAIN SIZZLE

... THE FLAMING,
TORRID HERO
THAT BURNS HIS
WAY THROUGH
FIFTY PAIR
OF UNDERWEAR
A DAY!

Captain SPAREPARTS

A HERO
SO BIONIC
THAT HE USES
ALUMINUM FOIL AS
TOILET TISSUE!

CAPTAIN TOAD

A FROG
PRINCE
HE'S NOT!

CAPTAIN TURNPIKE

HONK
IF YOU LOVE
FAST ACTION!
THIS ONE WILL
DRIVE YOU
WILD!

THE CRIMSON CAT

FINICKY FELINE PHANTOM OF THE NIGHT, TERRORIZER OF MICE AND MEN!

FAT BAT

A CAPED CRIMEFIGHTER SO FAT THAT HE'S KNOWN AS THE DYNAMIC DUO!

HITMAN

HE'LL MAKE YOU DIE LAUGHING-- OR ANY OTHER WAY THAT CROSSES HIS MIND!

THE HOODED ROBIN

MEDIEVAL SWASHBUCKLING HERO THAT TAKES FROM BOTH THE RICH AND THE POOR. TALK ABOUT FAIR PLAY!

Little Often Agony
AND HER USELESS, WEAK-STOMACHED DOG, *RETCH* !

Manduck the Magician

THE DAZZLING,
DEFT,
SUPERHERO
DEDICATED TO
TRUTH, JUSTICE
AND PRACTICE
FOR HIS
NIGHTCLUB ACT.

THE MASKED BERNARD

FOLLOW THE ADVENTURES
OF THIS *Wonder Dog*
OF THE MOUNTAIN TOPS
IN HIS NEVER-ENDING
SEARCH FOR A
FIRE HYDRANT !

THE MACHO HUNK

WATCH THIS
HULK OF IRE
CHANGE INTO A
GROTESQUE, UGLY
98 lb. WEAKLING
WHEN HE'S CALM !

Apeman
LORD OF THE
TREETOPS AND
GUINNESS RECORD
BOOK HOLDER FOR
VINE—SWINGING
COLLISIONS!

Beetle
Bail Jumper
JOIN THE FUN
AND GAMES WITH
THE HILARIOUS
GANG AT
HAHATTICA PRISON!

THE BLUE BLOWFISH
THE
POWDER-BLUE
DIP OF THE
DEEP...

CAPTAIN KID
DEDICATED TO
ALL THE THINGS
A GOOD LAD
SHOULD--EXCEPT
SCHOOLWORK!

SUPERDUD

HE'S A
BIRD-BRAIN!
HE'S PLAIN!
HE'S
SUPERDUD!

THE DERANGED LONER

COME WITH US NOW
TO THOSE THRILLING
DAYS OF YESTERYEAR...
YESTERYEAR?
WHENEVER!

CAPTAIN TRIVIAL

THE SUPERHERO
FOR THE MINOR
ANNOYANCES!
NO JOB IS TOO
SMALL FOR
CAPTAIN TRIVIAL

see
page
187

GUEST SHOT

YOU NEVER
KNOW WHO'S LIKELY
TO SHOW UP IN AN
INFERIOR BOOK
OF INFERIORS!

...BUT OTHER SINISTER SOURCES WERE AT WORK TO THWART *CAPTAIN TURNPIKE* IN HIS QUEST TO SAVE *PEGGY* AND THE KINDLY *MR. ADAMS* FROM THE SCOURGE OF THE ROADS, THE *PURPLE POTHOLE!*

UNKNOWN TO OUR HERO ONE OF P.P.'s HENCHMEN LIES IN WAIT...

...AS YOU REMEMBER,,THE CYNICAL **PROFESSOR BEERBELLY** OPENED A CHAIN OF MASSAGE PARLORS FOR GERMAN SHEPHERDS WHICH TIPPED OFF OUR HERO, THE **CRIMSON CAT**, THAT HIS ARCH-VILLAIN WAS UP TO NO GOOD!

THE TABBY CRIMEFIGHTER FOUND ONE IMPORTANT CLUE OVERLOOKED BY THE NAPOLEON OF CRIME -- THERE WERE NO **GERMAN SHEEP** WITHIN **700** MILES OF THE AREA!!

...AND MUCH LATER, WE FIND OUR HERO, THE **BLUE BLOWFISH** IN HIS SECRET UNDERWATER LAIR PREPARING HIS PILOT-FISH DEVICE WITH WHICH HE HOPES TO CAPTURE THE FIENDISH **DOCTOR FROGLIPS** BEFORE HE TURNS **BUDDY** AND **SUE** INTO JUMBO SHRIMP!

...MEANWHILE, *RAGOO* of the *JUNGLE* KNEW BY HIS HUNTER'S CUNNING THAT HIS QUARRY, *BIMBO*, KING OF THE ELEPHANTS, WAS NEAR!

THE *RAJAH OF KAMIR* WANTED THIS BEAST FOR A FEAST-- NEARLY EVERYONE HAD HEARD OF *RAGOO'S* SPAGHETTI WITH *ELEPHANT* SAUCE...

...AS YOU REMEMBER...
LITTLE OFTEN AGONY
AND HER FAITHFUL DOG
(AND SUSPECTED HALF-BROTHER),
RETCH ARE ON A SECRET
ASSIGNMENT TO ARREST THE
INFAMOUS RINGLEADER OF A
GANG THAT SELLS PARENTS
AS SLAVES TO A
PULVERIZING PLANT
SOMEWHERE IN THE
AMAZON JUNGLE!

WHAT HAPPENS THEN IS
TOO DISGUSTING
TO EXPLAIN HERE...

GREAT LEAPING
GIZZARD GUTS,
RETCH! IT SAYS
HERE **BRUNO THE
BUTCHER** MAY BE
INVOLVED!

GASP!
GIZZARD
GUTS!

...MEANWHILE... **CAPTAIN TURNPIKE** SPEEDS TOWARDS THE HIDEOUT OF THE **PURPLE POTHOLE**, THE FIENDISH ARCH-VILLIAN THAT KIDNAPPED **PEGGY** AND KINDLY OLD **MR. ADAMS** AND IS SLOWLY BRAINWASHING THEM TO TURN THEM INTO TOLL-BOOTHS!

UNKNOWN TO **CAPTAIN TURNPIKE** IS THE FACT THAT THE **PURPLE POTHOLE'S** HENCH-MEN LAY IN WAIT FOR HIM...

...SUDDENLY, THE **FAT BAT** SPOTS THE SHAPELY NEWSPAPER WOMAN, **AMELIA PULSEFIRE** (WHO IS THE ONLY LIVING PERSON WHO KNOWS THE SECRET IDENTITY OF OUR HERO--AND IS SECRETLY IN LOVE WITH HIS STOMACH!)

IN THE CLUTCHES OF THE RATHER OBSCURE VILLAIN, THE **GREEN BANANA** (WHOSE DIABOLICAL PLAN IS TO TRANSFORM THE ENTIRE CITY OF SACRAMENTO INTO SLAVES BY INJECTING THEM WITH HOME-MADE BANANA DACQUIRIS AND CHANGING THEM INTO ONE OF THE BUNCH!)

FAT BAT SWINGS INTO ACTION!

...**AT THE SAME MOMENT,** HIGH ATOP A MOUNTAIN, OUR FLAMING HERO, **CAPTAIN SIZZLE.** RESTS AFTER HIS NARROW ESCAPE FROM THE CLUTCHES OF THE FEMALE ARCH VILLAIN, **FOO WOMAN CHOO,** WHO AT THIS VERY MOMENT HAS CAPTAIN SIZZLE'S WONDER DOG, **TORRID,** IN HER TORTURE CHAMBER, RENDERING HIM INTO A BIONIC FIRE HYDRANT...

MEANWHILE, UNBEKNOWNST TO *CAPTAIN TOAD*, *SALLY* AND *SUE* ARE IN THE CLUTCHES OF THE EVIL *DOCTOR SWAMPGAS*, WHOSE DIABOLICAL PLAN IS TO TRANSFORM THE GIRLS INTO THE CURSE OF FEMININITY, *PERPETUAL PUBERTY!*

GOOD EVENING, *CAPTAIN TOAD*...

MENU

THE USUAL, PIERRE!

MENU

...BUT THE PRISON AREA WAS CLEARED OF MOST OF THE BODIES, AND THE FIRES SET BY THE INMATES HAD ONLY BURNED THREE MAIN BUILDINGS! THEREFORE, THE RIOT AT HAHATTICA STARTED BY FUN-LOVING *BEETLE BAIL-JUMPER*, AFTER STUFFING HIS MATTRESS DOWN A GUARD'S THROAT, *DID* SERVE *BEETLE'S* IMPISH WAY OF RIDDING HIS CELL-BLOCK OF ROACHES!

HAPPY BIRTHDAY, *BEETLE*, FROM YOUR MOTHER!

THANKS, SARGE...

OH, MAN--
WHAT A
WAY TO GO!

As you recall, the **DERANGED LONER** spent thirty days in the slammer for littering (*He left his calling card-- silver bullets--embedded in a local cattle baron's forehead!*)

And to top it off, **TWO TON TWO**, his fat ethnic companion, fell in love with the masked rider's faithful horse, **TINCUP**, and eloped!

...AND THE *HOODED ROBIN* DID INDEED SPLIT THE ARROW! BUT AS FATE WOULD HAVE IT, THE ARROW WAS EMBEDDED IN THE SHERIFF OF NOT-BACONORHAM'S CHEST AT THE TIME! SO, OUR SWASHBUCKLING HERO ESCAPED TO HIS FOREST REALM AND *MAID MARION* AS THE REST OF HIS FLOCK OF FEATHERED FRIENDS WATCHED AND TOLD THE TALE OF HOW THE *HOODED ROBIN* FIRST MET *JOHN BABY*...

...BUT THE WABONGA TRIBE DIDN'T COUNT ON THE **SPEED** OF APEMAN! AS THE LORD OF THE TREETOPS DARTS TOWARDS THE *HIDDEN CITY* OF THE *SIX IMMORTALS* TO RETURN THE OLD AND BEAUTIFUL JEWEL OF TIFFANY BEFORE THE HIGH PRIEST PLUCKS OUT THE BELLY-BUTTON OF THE APEMAN'S BRIDE WITH A DULL BUTTERKNIFE...

...MEANWHILE, LITTLE OFTEN AGONY AND HER WEAK-STOMACHED DOG, RETCH, SOMEHOW ESCAPED THE DEADLY FIRE IN THE OLD PEOPLE'S HOME! SHE WANDERED AIMLESSLY, AFTER WATCHING THE KINDLY, AGATHA CRUM— WELL, THROW HER ELECTRIC WHEEL— CHAIR INTO THE PATH ON AN ONCOMING FIRE ENGINE BECAUSE THEY DIDN'T KNOW THE PASSWORD, OR FOR THAT MUCH CARE WHAT IT WAS! BRUNO THE BUTCHER (WHO IS REALLY AN F.B.I. AGENT), IS NOW SCHEDULED TO BE HIT...

ZOONK WHIF **TH WOCK** ZAP BANG! TWANNG GNNGNNG B

ZZZPPT ZONKCH ZZZZNNG
ZING UGHHH! SWIISH THUD

RETCH
RETCH!

...MEANWHILE, *SUPERDUD* NOT ONLY STOPPED THE FIENDISH AND CRUDELY CLEVER NEWSPAPER COPY BOY, *TIMMY BOLSEN*, FROM GETTING OVERTIME PAY FOR WORKING ON HIS BIRTHDAY, BUT HE ALSO THWARTED ALL THE EFFORTS OF THE LOCAL DELICATESSEN FROM MAKING THE SANDWICHES LOOK THICK BY USING THOSE CRUNCHY LETTUCE STEMS AND FOLDING THE AMERICAN CHEESE IN HALF! ...THAT WAS YESTERDAY! TODAY...

...AND NOW FOR THE FIRST TIME THE **MASKED BERNARD** WAS FACE TO FACE WITH HIS LONG, LOST MASTER WHO HAD TO SELL HIM, AS A PUP, TO A TRIBE OF DOG-EATING SADISTS THAT ROAMED THE ALPS ON MOTORCYCLES WHO IN TURN TRADED HIM IN FOR A SUBSCRIPTION TO A TRASHY MAGAZINE...

THUD!

...AND A MOMENT LATER, *CAPTAIN TURNPIKE* BOLTS ALONG THE HIGHWAY AFTER ESCAPING THE CLUTCHES OF *DOCTOR DETOUR'S* EVIL HENCHMAN, THE INFAMOUS AND ALL-AROUND ROTTEN UP-AND-COMING VILLAIN, *MR. LUBEJOB!*

UNBEKNOWNST TO OUR HERO IS THE FACT THAT THE *PURPLE POTHOLD* HAS HIS THUGS SCANNING THE ROADS TO PREVENT *CAPTAIN TURNPIKE* FROM SAVING *PEGGY* AND THE KINDLY *MR. ADAMS* FROM THE FATE OF BEING TURNED INTO BUMPERSTICKERS!

...AND MILES AWAY, **BIMBO**, KING OF THE ELEPHANTS, HEARS **RAGOO** OF THE **JUNGLE** APPROACH!
THE CUNNING PACHYDERM HAS ELUDED OUR HERO SO AS NOT TO WIND UP AS AN INGREDIENT IN **RAGOO'S** SPAGHETTI WITH ELEPHANT SAUCE!
(Here's how to get this recipe, ALMOST, fans! Just shoot an elephant and send his remains and .75¢ TO **RAGOO**, °/₀ *This Book*)

PAINT

...BUT UNBEKNOWNST TO *MANDUCK THE MAGICIAN*... IS THE FACT THAT HIS SLIGHT OF HAND AND HYPNOTIC TRANCES ARE NO MATCH FOR THE ANGER OF ONE OF HIS NIGHTCLUB CUSTOMERS... ESPECIALLY WHEN THEY FIND SOMETHING IN THEIR SOUP...

...As you remember, **CAPTAIN KID** followed the **WART** (whom our hero discovered is a demented, retired truant officer) to the school's office. Where the sinister villain is in the process of stealing all the money collected for "*BAGELS AND ICE CREAM DAY...*"

...THE **BLUE BLOWFISH** BOLTS OUT OF HIS SECRET UNDERWATER LAIR, DIRECTING HIS FAMOUS FISHMOBILE IN THE DIRECTION OF **BUDDY** AND **SUE**, TRAPPED IN THE CLUTCHES OF THE DIABOLICAL **DR. FROGLIPS**, WHO PLANS TO TURN THEM INTO **ANCHOVIES !!**

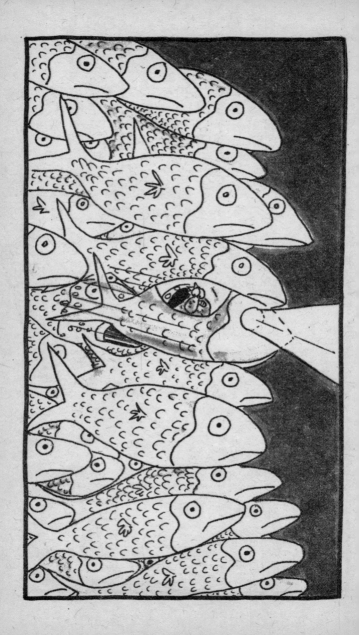

...BUT SUDDENLY, THE FIENDISH, DIABOLICAL, PRACTICAL JOKER, **DOCTOR GAGMAN**, BURSTS OUT OF HIS MURKY LABORATORY WITH YET **ANOTHER** PLOT TO THWART OUR HERO, THE *PINK FRUITFLY...*

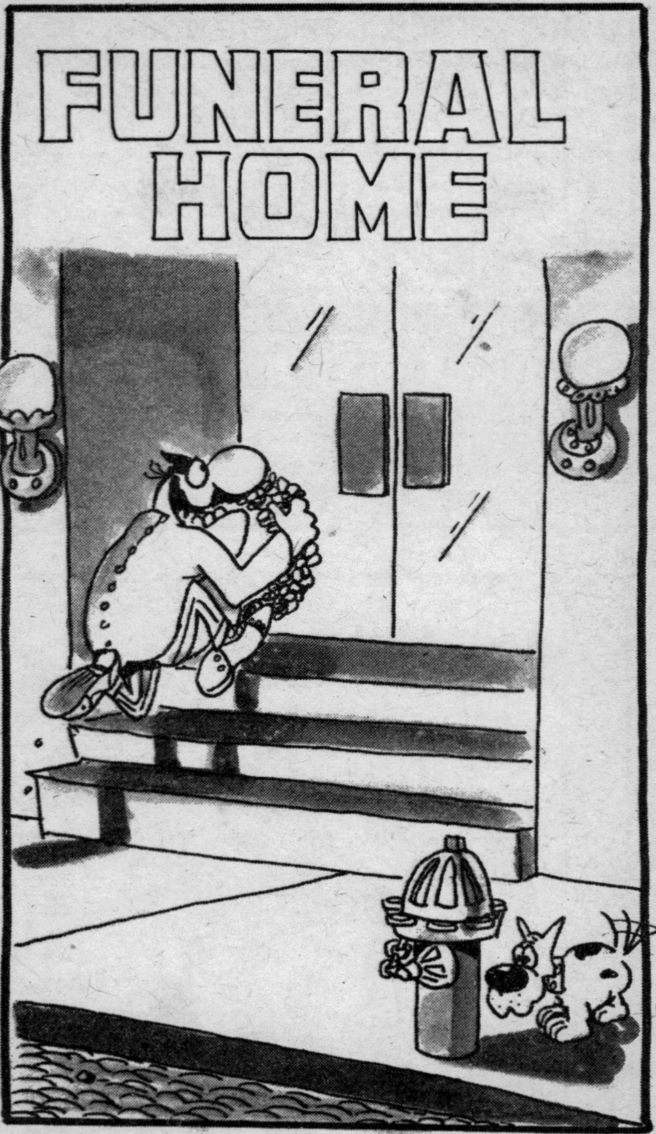
FUNERAL HOME

... AND MINUTES LATER, *THE PINK FRUITFLY* COMES TO PAY HIS RESPECTS..

...MEANWHILE, *CAPTAIN TURNPIKE* SEARCHES FOR *PEGGY* AND THE KINDLY *MR. ADAMS* NOT KNOWING THAT *DR. DETOUR* HAS JOINED FORCES WITH THE *PURPLE POTHOLE* TO FULFILL THEIR EVIL PLOT TO CHANGE THE ENTIRE CITY OF WALLA WALLA INTO THE SCOURGE OF HIGHWAYS -- *FLAGMEN!*

...BUT THE *APEMAN* DID ESCAPE THE DREADED HAIRY NOSTRIL PEOPLE OF OOMPA, ONLY TO FIND THAT THE LOST TRIBE OF POISONOUS ARM-PITS HAVE CAPTURED THE LORD OF THE TREETOPS *BRIDE!* THEY ARE AT THIS MOMENT ANOINTING HER TENDER UNDER-ARMS WITH THE DEADY FUNGUS FROM THE MUTTER PLANT! WE NOW JOIN *APEMAN* IN FAST FLIGHT TO THE RESCUE...

...**B**UT UNBEKNOWNST TO THE EVIL AND FIENDISH NAPOLEON OF CRIME, **_PROFESSOR BEERBELLY_**, IS THE FACT THAT THE **_CRIMSON CAT_**, TALENTED TABBY CRIME-FIGHTER, IS AT THIS MOMENT PUSSYFOOTING TOWARDS THE SINISTER VILLAIN'S VAULT TO SECURE HIS DIABOLICAL PLANS...

...SUDDENLY, *LITTLE OFTEN AGONY'S* AMNESIA DISAPPEARED AS SOON AS SHE SMELLED *BRUNO THE BUTCHER'S* AFTER-SHAVE LOTION -- WHICH HE SPRINKLES ON A LITTLE *TOO* PROFUSELY -- SINCE HE BELONGS TO THE SECRET ORGANIZATION THAT *NEVER* BATHES OR FREE THEMSELVES OF BELLY-BUTTON LINT, *THE OVER-FORTY BAD GUY LEAGUE,* WHO KIDNAP PARENTS AND LET DOGS RETCH ON THEIR FLOORS AND OTHER NASTY THINGS...

...As you remember, the fiendish and diabolically ugly arch villain, *Professor Disgusting*, stole the plans from our hero, *Captain Toad*, for the duplicating ray!
But what of the papers to put *Doctor Allen* and *Miss Smith* to sleep after donating their life-support machines to help needy Volkswagens?

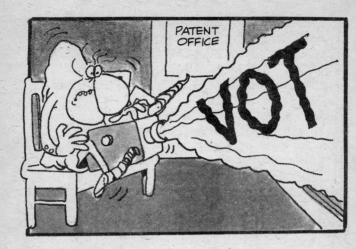

TO BE CONTINUED...

TO BE CONTINUED...

...BUT THE *HOODED ROBIN* AND HIS FLOCK OF FEATHERED FRIENDS WERE READY!

THEY KNEW THE SHERIFF OF NOBACON WOULD ENTER THE REALM OF THE *HOODED ROBIN'S* FOREST AND FALL PREY TO THE OUTLAW HERO'S NETWORK OF FEATHERED FRIEND'S ARROW TELEGRAPH SYSTEM...

TWANG!

SNAP!

RIP!

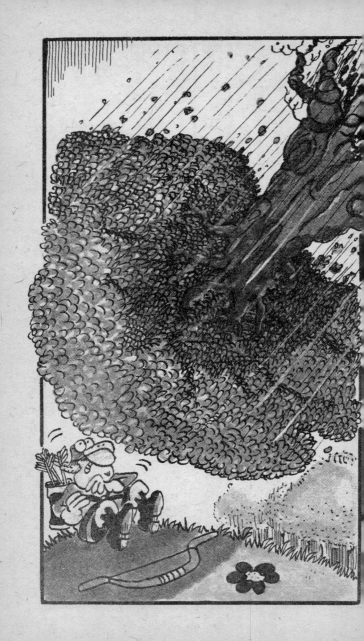

...SUDDENLY, **RAGOO OF THE JUNGLE,** KNEW THAT HIS QUARRY, **BIMBO,** KING OF THE ELEPHANTS, HAD GIVEN HIM THE SLIP!
UNBEKNOWNST TO OUR HERO IS THE FACT THAT THE **RAJAH OF KAMIR** WHO SENT HIM TO KILL THIS BEAST AND THEN PREPARE **RAGOO'S** SPAGHETTI WITH ELEPHANT SAUCE *(An old family recipe-- now sold in cans!)* WAS IN REALITY THE **SCOURGE OF KAMIR** IN DISGUISE WHO IS AFTER **RAGOO'S** RECIPE...

SNAP!

THANKS, SARGE...

ANY-TIME, BEETLE..

SARGE

...BUT *BRUCE BRANFLAKES* DID CHANGE INTO THE *MACHO HUNK* ANYHOW! AND HE *DID* TEAR UP ALL THE UNDERWEAR AT THE BROOKSIDE OLD PEOPLE'S HOME!
AND HE *DID* PULL THE LEGS OFF LITTLE TIMMY'S ANT COLONY!
NOW *BRUCE* IS LEFT WITH THE QUESTION--CAN IT BE TRUE THAT THIS *HUNK* IS ACTUALLY CONSERVATIVE?

...AND ELSEWHERE, WE FIND THE *BLUE BLOWFISH* RACING AGAINST TIME AS THE SEATRAIN *ZOOMS* TOWARDS THE *LOST KINGDOM* IN AN EFFORT TO ALTER THE EVIL *DR. FROGLIP'S* EXPERIMENT ON *BUDDY* AND *SUE* THAT CHANGED THEM INTO FRENCH FRIES...

...AND NOW WITH *LUCKY* AND *LILY* ON THE TRAIL OF THE NAPOLEON OF CRIME, THE INFAMOUS *PROFESSOR BEERBELLY*, OUR TABBY WONDER--THE *CRIMSON CAT*--WITH HIS FELINE MOVEMENTS AND GOLD FLECKS OF MOONLIGHT DANCING IN HIS EYES, LOWERS HIMSELF THROUGH THE SKYLIGHT OF HIS ARCH-VILLAIN'S HIDEOUT TO THWART HIS SECRET PLAN OF HORROR--TO GET THE MAYOR RE-ELECTED!

KREEK
KREEK
KREEK

WRRRRR

...*SUDDENLY A GANGMEMBER
OF THE SINISTER ARCH—
VILLAIN THE PURPLE POTHOLE
ZOOMS IN UPON OUR HERO
CAPTAIN TURNPIKE WHO IS
IN HOT PURSUIT IN AN EFFORT
TO SAVE PEGGY AND KINDLY
MR. ADAMS FROM BEING
TRANSFORMED INTO EXIT
RAMPS !*

...BUT SUDDENLY, THE MEEK, MILD BRUCE BRANFLAKES WHOM EVERYONE ON EARTH REALIZES BY NOW (*NO THANKS TO THE T.V. NEWS COVERAGE AND NEWSPAPER SPREADS, NOT TO MENTION THE VICTIMS OF DOWNTOWN TOLEDO!*) CHANGES TO AN EIGHT-FOOT, RAGING, MONSTER KNOWN AS *THE MACHO HUNK* WHENEVER HE FEELS LIKE IT, LATELY...

...AND ELSEWHERE, THE FIERY, INFERNO, **CAPTAIN SIZZLE** RETURNS TO HIS HOME AFTER HIS WONDER HOUND, **TORRID**, WAS CHANGED INTO A HOT DOG--WITHOUT MUSTARD!..

...AND NOW IT WAS UP TO **HITMAN**, AS IT **ALWAYS** IS WHEN ALL THE LAW ENFORCEMENT AGENCIES HAVE TO GO BEYOND THEIR CAPABILITIES *!*..

HITMAN, A MILD-MANNERED CITIZEN THAT CHOSE THIS PROFESSION BECAUSE HE CAN DO AN EXCELLENT HUMPHREY BOGART IMPRESSION, AND LOOKS GREAT IN BASIC BLACK! **HITMAN**--A GUY THAT THINKS THE **HIT PARADE** IS A MULTIPLE RUB-OUT CONTRACT...

...YOUR CONTRACT... **HIT TONY!**

Meanwhile, as all this nonsense is going on, Captain Klutz is sitting dejectedly in his secret hideout (not too far from Don Martin's studio) in Bayonne...

How could all those Almost Superheroes do their thing while I, Captain Klutz, the almost greatest Almost Superhero, sits dejectedly in my secret hideout in Bayonne!

RINGA RINGA